Serpentine

Michael Sagar-Fenton
with Stuart B Smith

First published in 2005 by Truran,
Croft Prince, Mount Hawke, Truro, Cornwall TR4 8EE
www.Truranbooks.co.uk
Truran is an imprint of Truran Books Ltd

ISBN 1 85022 199 5

Printed and bound in Cornwall by R Booth Ltd,
Antron Hill, Mabe, Penryn, Cornwall TR10 9HH

ACKNOWLEDGEMENTS
The author and publishers thank Stuart B Smith.

On the Lizard thanks to John Hendy and David Hill for sharing insights into the life and
times of serpentine turners so generously; also to Mrs Vera Hill, Peter Greenslade, Zena
Browning, Derek Pitman, Michael Casley and Ian Casley.

In addition thanks to Paul Turner, Trevor Lawrence, Mr and Mrs AG Oliver, Mr and Mrs J
Hodge, Julie and David Juniper and to all those who gave access to their private collections;
to Jonathan Holmes and Katie Herbert of Penlee House Gallery and Museum, Penzance and
Rob Cook of the Royal Cornwall Museum, Truro, the PCCs of St Grada, Grade, St Mary's,
Cadgwith, St Wynwallow, Lizard and St Marys, Penzance.

The author thanks Simon Turney for his diligent and merciless work on the text.

PICTURE CREDITS
Morrab Library Richards' Collection, Penzance pp 7, 17
Penlee House Gallery and Museum, Penzance pp 19, 33, 45
Peter Greenslade pp 9, 53, 54, 55, 56
Michael Sagar-Fenton pp 39, 46, 47, 63
Zena Browning cover, pp 32, 43
George Vaughan Ellis p 64
David Juniper back cover, p 62

Contents

Kynance Cove.

Introduction

The inspiration for this book came from my co-author Stuart B Smith OBE, industrial archeologist and polymath, former chief executive of the Trevithick Trust, for whom serpentine has been a lifetime's study and fascination. His material and researches have been the foundation of the book, and he might well have written it himself if he could have plundered the time from his many other interests. However he generously extended that opportunity to me, and I am pleased in return to dedicate this book to him.

It could have remained in the realm of desirable but unattainable projects if not given real and substantial shape by Jonathan Holmes, Access and Outreach Officer of Penlee House Gallery and Museum, Penzance. Jonathan Holmes' interest and endeavour included the setting up of the first major exhibition ever dedicated to the subject in Penlee House in November 2005. It was also decided that such a significant, previously unexplored area of Cornish industrial and social history was worthy of a publication.

My own interest in serpentine, and geology in general, started from a fairly low base. Inanimate stones do not – at first sight – do a lot to amuse the casual onlooker, and my immediate associations with serpentine were memories of low-grade 1960s souvenirs. But with a little knowledge and imagination, the world of quiescent rocks led me back to as dramatic a scenario as has ever existed; a planet full of Wagnerian fury, erupting, cooling, exploding once more, seas rising and falling, freezing and melting, giant continents moving in a stately dance, endlessly seeking equilibrium. We realise now more clearly than ever that the earth is not a relic but a living thing, subject to changes on which our very survival may depend. There is nothing dry about the study of our host planet.

The coloured varieties of serpentine evoke its violent genesis, freezing a liquid moment from the deeps of geological time. You can look at them and into them, your eye drawn below the surface to the once-churning depths, the highlights and crystals, veins and swirls, the subtle gradations of colour and form.

It is a bonus that we find these minerals beautiful, promoting the Lizard serpentine from just another piece of Cornwall's complex geological jigsaw puzzle to something unique. The stone ranges through delicate greens, light dun, yellow, bluish-purple to scarlet, brown and olive-black, with – in its natural state – many surface textures from a deep mat to a metallic shine. When worked by experts it can become a subtle piece of craft, a mass-produced souvenir, or a sheet of polished marble. It has been all these things in its time, and the story of its exploitation reflects our own changing times and tastes.

I hope readers will enjoy the tale, and that it will lead to a greater awareness and appreciation of the serpentine stone. I also hope that it will encourage readers to look at the whole Lizard peninsula with fresh eyes. As well as its natural magnificence, it retains an atmosphere all its own, almost untouched by the increasing speed of life around it. It is well worth the journey.

Michael Sagar-Fenton
Kemyel Crease   August 2005

The Lizard

The southern peninsula of West Cornwall known as The Lizard is still one of the best-kept secrets in an over-exposed county. Many thousands of people do descend on it every summer, to sit on the beaches of Kennack and Coverack, to admire the rugged beauty of Kynance Cove, to gaze at the mighty satellite dishes on Goonhilly Downs, or to go to the extreme end and stare out at the busy shipping lanes beyond. However it has never reached the saturation point of other parts of Cornwall. The Lizard is mainland Britain's most southerly point, but for some reason this does not inspire the same romantic appeal of its western extremity, Land's End, only some thirty-five miles away. Few people travel so far without making that ultimate pilgrimage.

The Lizard, by contrast, is served only by country lanes to the south of the modest market town of Helston, and appears to offer little – apart from its 'most southerly' status – not to be found elsewhere in Cornwall, in more accessible places. Yet beneath its skin lies one of the most complex land masses in Britain.

The Lizard is almost an island. Less than three miles separate the highest navigable waters of the Helford River at Gweek from Lowertown Helston, where ships once sailed up the Cober for tin before the perennial shingle of Loe Bar defeated them. It is a squarish block, about nine miles in either direction, with a large bite out of the south-eastern corner. It has coasts to all the main points of the compass, from the weather-blasted cliffs of the west and south to the gentler slopes to the east, with a north coast bordering the Helford River itself, almost English in its tree-lined valleys and creeks.

Cornwall is a county of micro-climates, and nowhere more so than on the Lizard. On the same day a family can picnic and swim in the calm airs of the Helford while great waves are beating spray into the air fifteen minutes' drive to the west.

If the surface is full of contrasts, the substructure is even more so. Even in small islands like Britain, one may expect a geological feature to extend for many miles before changing. But a geological map of the Lizard is a jigsaw of tiny and complex pieces, whose edges are sometimes still sharply distinguishable from each other. There are at least ten clearly distinct types of rock beneath the feet of anyone who travels from Helston to Gweek, by way of the Lizard and St Keverne, not counting the persistent deposits of flint on some of the beaches.

The range of mineral deposits covers an awesome spread of time. The islets just off the most southerly point, for example, are known as the 'Man Of War' reef, a unique sub-type of granite. The reef is one of the oldest objects in the British Isles, and in fact one of the oldest in the world, having burst out of the earth's mantle some 500 million years ago, predating the first corals, fish, or land-based plants.

Geological time is always difficult to envisage. Readers of this book may live to be a hundred. To an oak tree such hasty lives would pass by in a swift blur of movement. Generations of oak trees would have sprung up, matured and rotted since the ice ages, which ended only ten thousand years ago. Primitive humans first appeared two million years ago, while dinosaurs flourished from two

A serpentine turner, thought to be Mr Paul, picured by his lathe, showing some of the lighthouses he has made.

hundred and thirty to about a hundred million years ago, before their sudden decline. Sharks put our paltry pedigree to shame, dating from over three hundred and seventy-five million years ago. To put one's hands on a piece of stone which has weathered the deep oceans, the sea, air, winds and storms for five hundred million winters is still a profound thrill, a connection to a dizzying spiral of time. We feel a thrill of antiquity on seeing the remains of civilisations a few thousand years old, but it is estimated that, between the birth of the Man Of War reef and that of the mainland rocks of Lizard Point on which we stand to look at it – which once belonged to a different continent – the earth revolved around the sun a hundred and fifty million times. No wonder our minds can hardly contain the thought.

The Lizard has peculiar features which give clues to its past. No-one who crosses it can fail to notice the flatness of its plateau. It does slope very slightly upwards from the most southern point to the northern boundary where the granite hills of Carnmenellis begin to intrude, but rises less than a hundred feet in fifteen miles, almost imperceptible to the eye. This indicates that the central moors were once under water and rose slowly from the depths. The sight of such a bare unrelieved plain is most affecting, even in the pleasant days of summer, and in winter it is easy to believe the legends of a terrible battle between God and Satan on Goonhilly Downs which so blasted the earth that nothing would ever grow there again. It seemed entirely appropriate when the monstrous dishes of the Goonhilly telecommunication station were placed there, giant structures in perfect proportion with the brutal landscape around them.

A less obvious but equally striking feature is the alignment of the Lizard in relation to the prevailing weather. The whole of Cornwall,

especially the far west, has been sculpted by wind, rain and waves which have driven from west to east over miles of Atlantic Ocean. This process has broken down the south-western extremity to a weather-beaten granite prow, presenting a narrow target to the constant attrition. Except, as the map shows, for the lower toe of the distinctive claw of Mount's Bay. The Lizard peninsula defies the elements with a mighty rock wall placed at right-angles to the stream of weather, the immovable post facing the irresistible force. This is assaulted every winter by a succession of storms, massive waves, and winds of a hundred miles an hour or more bearing horizontal, slashing rain. And yet, though scarred in places, it seems unmoved, standing as tall and strong as if it had arrived from another planet.

And in a way it did, not from another world, but from a vastly different part of this one.

The mysteries of tectonic movement and continental drift have only recently been understood. We have experienced earthquakes, volcanoes and other disturbances throughout history, but it has taken time to realise that the rock-solid continents we inhabit are not fixed in their relative positions, either to the earth's core or to each other. Ultimate time-lapse photographs of the earth's surface would show not only water levels rising and falling and ice sheets growing and diminishing, but simply everything in constant motion. Europe and America, for example, are still racing apart at a rate of 20mm a year. The seemingly orderly surface of the world is built on fluid chaos, from which jolting adjustments and boiling magma may emerge at any time. The shapes on our maps are merely the latest state of play.

Understanding this, it is not so surprising – although still hard to grasp – that the land mass we know as the Lizard came into being about thirty degrees to the south of the Equator.

The historic super-continent of the southern hemisphere, which once encompassed Africa, South America, Australia and Antarctica, has been named Gondwana. Between it and its northern neighbour – now North America and Europe – lay a wide channel, the Rheic Ocean. Following a disturbance beneath its depths some 350 million years ago, a mass of molten rock began to rise from the conjunction of the earth's crust and mantle, and ascend like a giant fiery bubble. As it rose it accumulated a cross-section of the geology it encountered on the way: other igneous rocks, volcanic lava, and sedimentary rocks from the earth's surface. It broke through to the sea bed with great violence, established itself as a discrete entity on the ocean floor, and lay there slowly cooling.

Meanwhile the slow drift of the two super-continents was carrying them inexorably towards each other, and the Rheic Ocean was squeezed into a narrow strait. When they finally collided, the rock mass of the Lizard was caught between them, and was slowly crushed. The stone, compressed between the hammer and the anvil of two vast land masses, heated up once more and went through another violent metamorphosis. In this state it was eventually welded onto the northern bank of the strait with tremendous force.

For a while – geologically speaking – it became a tiny part of the area known as Pangea. Then, when the continents divided again it hitched a ride on the super-continent of Laurasia, which headed slowly but determinedly northwards. The Lizard drifted across the Equator 250 million years ago, and the Tropic of Cancer less than 100 million years ago. Laurasia slowly defined itself into the familiar shapes of Europe and Asia. By the time the Lizard arrived at fifty degrees north, its current location, the waters had risen to isolate the British Isles from mainland Europe.

Typical Lizard landscape.

It remained grafted to the south-western tip of England, still in effect a foreign body amalgamated to the natural rocks of that region.

Their attachment occurred long ago, but the incident is still so geologically fresh that, on parts of the peninsula, the scars still show. The superficial flora give a clue to inner divisions. The range and diversity of the wildflowers of the peninsula deserve a book of their own, and there is a heather – the Cornish Heath – unique to the Lizard. But plants favour different subsoils, and you can see valleys in which one side is clad in a completely different vegetation from the other, and you can walk over hidden faults which wear their distinguishing mark in their plants and even butterflies and birds.

To the geologist the whole county of Cornwall is a selection of competing attractions. To the amateur it gives a chance to study the largest variety of minerals in the smallest space in the British Isles. To the professional its deposits of recoverable and marketable quantities of tin, copper, arsenic, lead, silver and gold as well as slate, granite and roadstone gave it the rich industrial base which has been such an important strand in its history.

The Lizard peninsula demonstrates this diversity in miniature. And the jewel in the Lizard's crown is its central core, the deposits of the coloured stone known to us as serpentine.

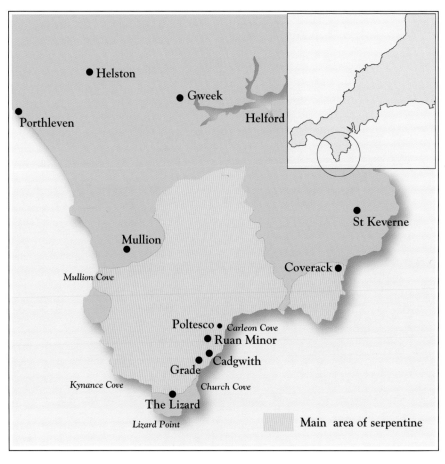

Coloured Rocks

Serpentine is essentially a marble. Marble is a class of rock which has – as described above – undergone at least two stages of metamorphosis: firstly its original formation, and then by being subjected to huge forces of heat and compression, which squeeze and concentrate the original materials so profoundly as to form a new crystalline structure. This process is that of a plutonic blender, mashing, pressing, exploding, mixing and finally cooling into deposits of more or less consistent material.

The charm, fascination and – for those who work in it – frustration of the Lizard variety of serpentine lies in its inconsistency. The forces which made it were random, and the materials in its makeup vary enormously in age as well as type. Some later types of rock have filled the gaps and cracks left in the former, causing banding of various widths.

Many larger crystals pepper the finer material. Trace elements of different minerals occur in unpredictable concentrations.

Serpentine is not rare. The Lizard is not the only place in Britain – or even in Cornwall – where it occurs. There is a small deposit near Polyphant by Bodmin Moor, and there are outcrops in Wales, Scotland and the Shetland Isles. Worldwide it is found in France, Germany, Spain, Portugal, Canada, and a deposit in Australia some four hundred miles in length. It is common in the United States, especially the earthquake state of California, where it is the 'state rock' and various websites offer advice on how to garden in its difficult soil. It is not popular with gardeners or farmers, as the surface crumbles into a fine impervious clay which tends to become waterlogged, and resists

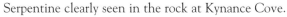

Serpentine clearly seen in the rock at Kynance Cove.

cultivation. The almost lunar landscape of parts of the Lizard plateau is not only due to exposure to the weather, but to its defiantly sterile surface, which only specialised ground-hugging plants have learned to exploit.

However it seems that the deposits in other parts of the world were not subject to quite the same degrees of disturbance as those on the Lizard. Most deposits are of a deep green olivine rock, with little variety. The uniqueness of the Lizard's deposit lies in its unpredictable range of structure and colour. It occurs nowhere else on earth.

Technically the stone is described as an 'ultra-basic magma', which means that it was extruded from the earth's mantle. Its composition varies, but it is basically a magnesium silicate. It is hydrated, i.e. it contains a relatively large proportion of water (and acid) within its crystals. Variation occurs in the traces of different metals mixed haphazardly up within it. As weathering exposes the metals they oxidise and the colours depend on the presence and proportion of the oxidised metals. This is not the whole story, as often the mixture is veined with other intrusive materials, or weaker strands of the same material, which show as fine superficial lines and clefts, rather like a map. Rocks will often cleave on these lines of weakness, leaving a thin sheen of colour on the whole of one surface. In places the evidence of continental drift or earthquake can be seen, where one deposit has rubbed against another, leaving a naturally smooth and polished surface, known locally as 'slickensides'.

A typical composition of serpentine has been reckoned at:

Silica	42.50%
Magnesium	38.50%
Water and acid	13.57%
Iron oxide	2.12%
Chromium oxide	1.36%
Aluminium	1.00%
Manganese oxide	0.70%
Lime	0.25%

Traces of asbestos, copper and other minerals are often present.

Lizard serpentine occurs in three principal types. The largest deposits are of bastite, the serpentine which most people would recognise, often bearing large crystals and a variety of colours. The bastite was the central core of the original 'bubble' of stone from which the Lizard was formed, and its structure shows that it cooled fairly slowly. Its basic geology is consistent, but its coloration can vary over a wide spectrum from red to green, to occasionally yellow or purplish, in random mixtures.

Tremolite serpentine borders the bastite to the north-east and south-west. This was forced into interaction with other bordering deposits. It is more compressed and disturbed, finer of grain and crystal, often banded, heavier, sometimes a dark green, often a deep rich red, although not usually used for ornamental purposes. It forms a large part of the exposed cliffs between Kynance Cove and Mullion.

The third type, dunite, is found in comparatively small deposits, usually on the boundaries between the main serpentine mass and the neighbouring rocks, very fine-grained and either a fairly consistent light brown or mixed with olivine to form a dense rock of deep green, almost black.

It is worth mentioning briefly the other main types of stone to be found on the peninsula (although the less geologically-inclined may wish to skip to the beginning of the next chapter). They are easiest to see where the sea slices into them and leaves them as either seashore rocks, spectacular cliffs, or the profusion of pebbles and boulders which lie on the beaches.

The upper part of the area, roughly north of a line from Mullion to Helford, is the natural local slate, itself only a part of Cornwall's patchwork, known (from its geological era, not as a slight to its host) as Devonian slate. South of the Helford and covering the Meneage area is a crush zone of mixed granite, slate and other random boulders, the result of the mighty prehistoric collision.

The distinctive fault line, the boundary between the Lizard proper and the shores of ancient Euramerica, runs visibly between Polurrian Cove (just north of Mullion) to Porthallow, by St Keverne, on the opposite coast, in a convex bulge. The land to the south of this is primarily made up of the serpentine core. However, on its way to the surface, and during its conjunction with the rest of Cornwall, large quantities of other material were displaced, picked up, moved around, often reconstituted, and re-deposited.

Principal among these were the schists, an unlovely word deriving from a Greek word meaning 'able to be split', the original rocks of the ocean floor beneath which the serpentine bubble formed, and through which it forced its furious way. They are of two distinct types, those resulting from cooled lava flows, hornblende schists, and those resulting from fossilised sedimentary deposits, mica schists. The heat and pressure of the process caused them to melt and re-crystalise. They form laminated layers which are often twisted and curved into fantastic folds and waves, easily seen in the cliffsides.

Around the St Keverne area, in a wide band which also reaches the sea between Kennack Sands and Black Head, is a smooth speckled granite known as gabbro. Nearby, principally at Coverack, is a red crystal-bearing rock called trocolite, locally known because of its appearance as 'troutstone'. Gabbro comes from the earth's crust, beneath the schists, while trocolite comes from a layer beneath that again, the moho layer, between the crust and the mantle, a thin molten sandwich of igneous rock rarely seen on the surface. Both of these were also forced up by the rise of the serpentine mass. There are also areas of ancient granite gneiss, including the very tip of the peninsula, while the offshore reefs are believed to be scrapings from the other side of the ancient supercontinental vice, Gondwana.

On the beaches of the coves, and in the walls of the older houses, the residue of millions of years lies in a fascinating mixture of ages and types. The houses were often made of beach stones, and these could include any of those mentioned above, along with chunks of attractive grey basalt, quartz, flint, and a solid aggregate containing bits of random stone, shells, and anything else which was caught up and melted together in the furnaces of time. Together they form a spectrum of colour and texture, history, geography, geology, and further clues to the mysteries of the earth.

Once alerted to the secrets of the landscape, it is difficult not to be distracted at every turn by the stories in the stones.

Selling Serpentine

'What should they know of England who only England know?' asked Kipling, and it is an open question when and how the natives of the southern Lizard peninsula became aware that the stone they took for granted as their normal environment was considered attractive by outsiders.

There are one or two improbable legends. One suggests that an unnamed shipwrecked sailor first noticed the colours polished by cattle on a field rub-stone (farmers often erected a single large stone in the middle of a field for the cows to itch themselves against). This 'eureka' moment has little credibility, since, as anyone who walks the Lizard's footpaths knows, nearly every stile in the serpentine area is polished by the centuries of human traffic. The cobbles in the old farmyards shine with every variety of colour, especially after a shower of rain. It is the business of farmers occasionally to split stones in order to remove or use them, thus revealing their internal hues. The locals would have to have been blind indeed to fail to spot their bright heritage over the millennia of their occupation.

The first documented reference to the working of serpentine concerns a Mr Drew from Penzance, who was engaged to carry out some repairs on the Lizard lighthouse in 1828, which required him to live for some time in the village. In his spare time (winter evenings can be long at the Lizard) he is reputed to have made a hobby of carving serpentine, and apparently made various items, both useful and ornamental. Penzance, and the Drew family, feature later in the story. But there is no suggestion that he invented the art, but rather that he learned it from a long and well-established local tradition.

The first practical use of the stone was some centuries earlier. As already mentioned it was picked up and worked into building stone for dwellings and farm buildings, hedges, stiles, gateposts, cobbles and any other purpose suitable for local stone. Most spectacularly it was quarried for the building of several church towers. Mullion, Grade, Ruan Minor and Landewednack church towers are mostly constructed of large dressed blocks of unpolished serpentine rock, sometimes in alternating courses with granite, and other Lizard churches have random blocks in their walls.

A grand elaborate jug from a catalogue – see the photograph opposite.

The occupants of the serpentine areas would have considered themselves ill-favoured by fortune. The concentrated deposits formed a sterile surface unfit for cultivation, and the rock itself was devoid of the mineral wealth notable in other parts of the county. Since recorded history began Cornwall has been famous for its large deposits of recoverable minerals. Tin and copper were the most common, but many other resources, such as arsenic and china clay, ensured that Cornwall's history was not that of a remote and barely inhabited peninsula but a centre of industry, trade, and mechanical innovation.

A deposit of copper near Mullion led to the opening of the southern Lizard's only recognisable mine in 1847 (Wheal Unity or Goosecroft), but it proved short-lived, and apart from exploratory workings in search of copper and china clay, the substructure of the peninsula appeared to be barren and worthless. The only exception was the extraordinary material known as 'soap-stone' or 'soapy rock', found in quantity in only one locality, Gew-graze on the western coast. This odd mineral has a smooth, soapy feel due to an abundance of talc in its makeup, and is so soft it can sometimes be crushed in the hand. It was created by the action of acids in the margins between the serpentine and dykes of feldspar granite, and was celebrated far beyond the Lizard for its novelty value. Its quarrying is believed to have begun as early as 1750. Even Josiah

Wedgwood became interested and investigated the possibility of its use in ceramics. However the deposits were very limited and the Gew-graze quarry was virtually worked out by 1819.

The earliest mentions of worked serpentine do not refer to a primitive art, but to what had clearly already become a small-scale industry. If Mr Wedgwood found it worth his while to travel to the Lizard to examine soap-stone in 1818, it is unlikely that the relatively huge deposits of serpentine had escaped the attention of those looking for other minerals to exploit. Serpentine's popularity would have been tempered by its contradictory virtues. It varies from hard to easily workable. Though durable, it is prone to weathering. Its very virtues depend on its variation of colour and texture, effectively its flaws. It requires patience, knowledge and experience to work successfully, and without a ready market there was little reason for these to be widely taught.

But a combination of factors in the middle years of the nineteenth century rapidly transformed the situation. The early Victorian era was a proud, confident and successful one, especially in industry, commerce and engineering. Queen Victoria and Prince Albert were also anxious to promote England as an international centre of culture and craft, an impulse which led to the Great Exhibition of 1851.

Grandad Bosustow working on the Lizard showing a good range of his work, from a lighthouse and a large bowl to much smaller pieces.

Well-to-do English families (educated by the cultural 'gap year' of the time, the Grand Tour) traditionally sought their cultural icons in the classical antiquities and artefacts of Europe. Great, and aspiring, houses in England demanded marble artefacts such as pillars, columns, mantlepieces, fireplaces, as well as ornamental items such as pedestals, urns, vases, tazzas (wide goblet-like drinking vessels) and other formal displays. In a small way, the quarries and workers of the Lizard began to compete with foreign suppliers for the supply of these desirable things.

Originally they merely provided the raw material. Several quarries were opened up for the purpose of cutting and exporting blocks in their natural state. They were sent by boat to monumental masons and marble works 'up-country' (and also to the Pearce family of monumental masons in Truro) to be made

into whatever the market demanded. But at the same time a fledgling industry was growing at home. A thorough geological survey of the area had been carried out by Henry de la Beche, a brilliant, eccentric amateur who was eventually sponsored by the government in 1832 to survey the whole of Cornwall. His findings set the standard for subsequent work, not least on the Lizard. He encouraged further and deeper quarrying, particularly at Signal Staff Hill near Cadgwith, which he said had already provided 'blocks of fair dimensions from which chimney-pieces have been cut'. This, he thought, would be a better proposition than the current use of 'weathered fragments chiefly now employed in the few ornamental works executed in this material'. His report was published in 1839.

Large quarried chunks were, as de la Beche

had predicted, readily extracted from the old diggings with the aid of modern mining and quarrying technology. They were soon on their way to a more local destination. The transformation from a cottage industry to an industry proper, organised, funded, and ready to take the risks familiar to mineral enterprises in Cornwall would be a quantum leap. The ideal opportunity was supplied by the closure of the Wherry Mine a few hundred yards west of Penzance harbour, an area still known as Wherrytown.

Wherrytown works in Penzance.

Penzance

Wherry Mine was itself an extraordinary enterprise, actually standing in the sea. Its head-works were built on a tidal reef some way offshore, a wooden turret protected by a stone breakwater, connected by a wooden staging to the shore. Doubtless the waters of Lariggan stream were originally used for power, but in the 1790s a steam engine was erected. The mine came to a dramatic halt when some of the superstructure was demolished by a ship adrift in a storm in 1798. Several efforts were made to revive the mine, but in 1840 the remaining assets were sold at auction.

This derelict site was bought and developed by three Penzance businessmen, John Organ, John Bromley and Richard Millet, apparently with the encouragement of the same Mr Drew, the lighthouse repairman who had made the rock his hobby in 1828. Stone was ordered from the Lizard quarries and shipped across the bay, and a large new factory building was erected. Most of the demand was for large polished slabs, but more intricate designs were also carved to order, often copies of classical designs. As yet there was no railway and all goods had to be shipped once again from the harbour, but the business flourished. By 1848 it was reported that thirty-seven men were employed there, many of them no doubt imported from the Lizard along with its native stone.

Two years earlier the business had been favoured by an enormous stroke of good fortune, in the form of patronage by the Royal Family. They were enjoying a holiday cruise off the coast of Cornwall, when Prince Albert, reputedly feeling seasick, asked to be put ashore on the Lizard. His boatman landed him in Kynance Cove. There he was met by a local hero who – in true Cornish tradition – did not fail to point out the unique products of that area. He showed the prince a few serpentine artefacts; even, according to some sources, sold him one or two. Albert was impressed, both by the quality of the stone itself and by the discovery of an English marble of which he had been unaware. After recovering from his malaise he then organised a visit to Wherrytown with the queen and the royal children in order to inspect the factory in person. Their patronage was sealed by an order for mantlepieces and pedestals for Osborne House, the elegant royal retreat then being built on the Isle of Wight.

Plans for the Great Exhibition were in the air. Its main purpose was to show that England could rival and surpass France, whose pre-eminence in the art industry was then unchallenged. The grandiose plans went ahead with extraordinary speed, and in May 1851 the Queen opened the huge glass and iron exhibition hall – soon known as the

'Crystal Palace' – in Hyde Park. The hall was 1848 feet long, 408 feet wide and up to 108 feet high to enclose whole trees. Anxieties were raised about the effect on the structure of vibration caused by the size of the crowd it would hold (as echoed more recently by the Millennium Bridge), but these were disproved by the delightful method of ordering a detachment of soldiers to carry out such manouevres as walking randomly backwards and forwards, marching in step, and jumping simultaneously into the air. More famous was the problem of the sparrows in the enclosed trees, whose droppings threatened to pollute the world's most precious artefacts. This was reputedly solved by the Duke of Wellington whose advice to the Queen consisted of the economic phrase 'Sparrow-hawks, Ma'am.'

Half the space was allocated to British products, and half to the rest of the world. Altogether there were seventeen thousand exhibitors, showing items as diverse as fine lace and hydraulic presses, huge carpets and the finest filigree ornaments. The Crystal Palace was visited by a staggering six million people before being dismantled, and the profits were put towards buying the land and building the museums at South Kensington – including of course the 'Victoria and Albert'.

Among the prize winners, for a pair of serpentine obelisks and a carved font, was John Organ of Penzance. The obelisks were replicas of Cleopatra's Needle, 13 feet high, and the font featured elaborate carved bosses on all its sides, supported by five decorated columns, later sent to an exhibition in New York. Among their other exhibits was a large hand-carved (by Arthur Harvey of Penzance) Bacchanalian vase. A reviewer noted approvingly:

Now that attention is directed to the serpentine rock, we have little doubt that it will be largely employed.

Drew's serpentine works on the front at Penzance, close to the present-day Queen's Hotel.

He was right. The exhibition was a triumph for the company. Although their products hardly outshone the finest and rarest marbles in the world, they had two advantages. Most of the objets d'art on show were known to connoisseurs from their European travels, but few of them had been adventurous enough to include West Cornwall in their itineraries. The multi-hued British serpentine came as a surprise and a novelty to those jaded by the display of so many of the world's familiar treasures, and was noted by several commentators. The other advantage was of course the approval already shown by the Royal Family, whose personal enthusiasm was noted by other great families of England. Orders flowed in for items destined for Westminster Abbey, Hampton Court, Chatsworth House, and numerous other public and private buildings, and churches. Customers included the Royal Family themselves who ordered further items for Osborne House, the Duke of Devonshire, the Marquis of Westminster, the Earl of Darnley and many others.

The commissions were not for minor ornaments but for pieces on a Victorian scale, in proportion with their settings. Great pedestals, large turned or spiral columns, fireplaces, pillasters, urns, obelisks and other monumental items were the objects of desire. The red serpentine was the most favoured, and large sheets of this dark polished material were required to satisfy the taste of the time.

The company had not anticipated such demand and could hardly cope, particularly with the administrative and marketing side, from Penzance. A partnership was formed with a group of London businessmen, and the company was incorporated as the London and Penzance Serpentine Company in 1851, with offices at 5 Waterloo Place, Pall Mall. A year later the London partners bought control of the company, and John Organ became its general manager.

A large serpentine vase on a plinth. It is made of hard serpentine which would not be worked now as it would take too long and there is a considerable risk of shattering.

The Lizard

On the misty Lizard, the demand led to the prospecting and opening up of several new quarries. The finding of deposits sufficiently pure to create the larger pieces was a continual headache. But the rewards were great. For the first time in its history the Lizard was enjoying mineral wealth, with the prospect of widespread employment and prosperity. The formerly cursed land was yielding unexpected riches.

There was another unexpected dividend, as professional journalists and writers, as well as gentlemen travellers and diarists – mainly, it seems, under-employed vicars – went west to discover the origin of the stone which had captured the fancy of the great and good. The Lizard became, in a small way, a fashionable destination – something which even its most loyal admirers would never have anticipated. Its desolation was not to the taste of all, but others responded to its wild beauty, the richness not only of its geology but also its equally fascinating botany and wildlife. Large stately houses began to appear among the huddled cottages. A faltering tourist trade was born. In 1854 the *Illustrated London News* sent an explorer to England's wildest extreme, who, after reviewing the serpentine works, reported:

At the Lizard Town – which, like its subsoil, may be regarded as a primitive formation – there was but indifferent accommodation for travellers. But near the ancient mud hovels an inn making up several beds has recently been erected; and the tourist may obtain tolerable accommodation at the inn at Cadgwith Cove and a few farm-houses in the neighbourhood.

It was hardly a glowing testimonial, and the plainness of Lizard Town was destined to receive a similarly bad press from then onwards, being described for example as *a dreary place where pigs wander about the streets with an air of majestic satisfaction* by Alphonse Esquiros in 1865. But travellers soon discovered the prettier coves on the sheltered east side, the Helford, the headlands of the west coast, and above all the elemental magnificence of Kynance Cove. They reported their discoveries with the enthusiasm and joy of pioneers. The Lizard was on the map. Its inhabitants began to realise that fortune had smiled on them, and looked for ways to exploit it further.

One way was to step up production of their own domestic product. Hand-turned and carved serpentine ornaments had enjoyed only a limited market before 1851, and profited immensely from the nascent tourist trade. Those who came to look at serpentine in its natural state often went home with a bag full of crafted souvenirs, which ranged from buttons to ink stands, ash trays, perhaps even the first lighthouses, and other portable objects.

But these were – at the time – relative chicken feed compared to the lucrative commissions for which their raw blocks of stone were being exported. For the first time some competition for the best stone emerged. It was not then in a state of shortage, but the quality was always variable and the increasing demand made the more thoughtful stone workers wonder whether their reserves would eventually become scarce, with the profits – as with so many previous mineral enterprises – benefiting only those far from the source of production. It soon occurred to them that the

Grade church is mostly built of serpentine blocks.

added value of turning their raw materials into works of art and craft need not be undertaken 'abroad', a designation which would certainly have included Penzance as well as Truro. The logical next step was to set up production as close as possible to the supply, and to provide the Lizard with something it had never before experienced, a major enterprise and industry of its own.

A handsome pair of vases in red serpentine.

Poltesco

The Lizard did not offer many suitable sites for a factory.

There was a well-established workshop at Kynance Cove powered by a small waterwheel. This had probably been operating since the turn of the nineteenth century, the source of the ornaments which had caught Prince Albert's eye. But anywhere on the western and southern coasts was out of the question for a larger enterprise due to the ferocity of the prevailing weather.

A sizeable stream was the first essential, as water power was the only option. There were no mines on the Lizard from which to inherit such valuable plant as a steam engine, as there had been in Wherrytown. A navigable and reasonably sheltered cove was next, since land transport was still completely impractical. The site needed to be within the serpentine area itself, and as close to existing quarries as possible.

Carleon Cove at the mouth of Poltesco Valley was an obvious choice. Its steep wooded valley contained a lively stream which drained most of Goonhilly Downs, and it already hosted some light industry. Two local mills up in the valley took advantage of the rushing water, of which one may already have seen service for turning the lathes for small scale serpentine production. The cove itself was devoted to a long-established pilchard fishery.

A fishing port on the Lizard required only a cleft in the wall of cliffs, a sloping shingle beach, and reasonable access from the landward side. The boats landed their catches on the beach and, when necessary, were drawn up above high water on wooden rollers

A coloured postcard showing the works at Poltesco.

or skids. A capstan turned by teams of fishermen hauled them up the shingle. In Carleon Cove as in several others this was housed in a round granite building. A few fish cellars for pressing and packing the pilchards had also arisen beside the beach, together with a couple of small cottages. A good cart track had been laid from the mill down to the cove. The little settlement might have continued to grow and prosper until it became a fully-fledged fishing village in its own right, except for the proximity of Cadgwith, whose geography it closely resembled. Possibly the offshore Poltesco rock might have been a discouraging factor. In any case by the 1850s it had been largely abandoned in Cadgwith's favour, and was ready for a new development. Like most useful land on the Lizard it was owned by a large land owning family, in this case the Vyvyans of Trelowarren.

The local entrepreneurs obtained financial backing, and the Lizard Serpentine Company was formed in 1853, under the general management of Henry Cox. In a later report it claimed that the company *did not in the first instance intend to manufacture, but they found it necessary to change their plan in order to introduce the stone into general use*. This may have been diplomatic, but was far from the truth. Large scale quarrying and export of serpentine was a growing industry, but the stone was being *introduced to general use* effectively enough by the existing factory in Penzance. There is little question that the motive behind the formation of the Lizard Serpentine Company was to offer them some stiff competition.

The company quickly set about the building and engineering works necessary to set the factory up.

One task was to create a new reservoir in the valley to give a good head of water to power the new water wheel. It was a familiar job to anyone involved in Cornish industry, and the labouring gangs soon produced a substantial dam. The wheel was to be 'over-shot', i.e. the

Poltesco works showing the waterwheel and stream.

water would pour onto it from above rather than turning it from below, and a series of sluices, leats, and launders soon arose to supply a stream from the reservoir or divert it when not needed.

The shingle beach may have served its purpose for fishing, but was not practical for loading larger vessels with heavy and precious pieces of masonry, and so work also began to construct a long wooden jetty. This would have been no easy task in exposed tidal waters, but a level platform was needed from the factory to the ships, strong and secure. For the larger schooners even this was too shallow at most states of the tide. Eventually, as the factory's output grew, a small fleet of flat-bottomed ferries was built to transport the products from the jetty to the schooners, while they waited at anchor a hundred yards or so offshore.

The factory grew in stages. The water wheel was made by Toys of Helston, an iron frame with wooden arms and buckets, 25 feet in diameter and 4 feet wide, housed on a timber framework. It stood furthest from the sea and discharged into the existing stream. Next to it a network of workshops began to spread towards the shore. The larger blocks of raw stone were cut into slabs for mantlepieces, shop-fronts etc, simply by sawing laboriously with a large, fine-toothed saw, originally by hand and later by machinery, cooled by a continuous trickle of water. A little grit helped the process, and the workers would drop in a little sand from the beach whenever they passed by. Some of the workshops were devoted to lathes, for turning the pillars, urns, candlesticks etc. Space was also required for the more elaborate works, the hand carving by the most skilled workers using traditional sculptors' tools. Unskilled labourers undertook the movement of blocks, the basic donkey-work of sawing and rough shaping, the eternal labour of the initial grinding and smoothing, packing the finished articles cushioned by straw in wooden cases, and transporting them to the boats. The finishing work was the preserve of fine craftsmen, mostly professional monumental masons, many experienced in church work from the

A close up view of the waterwheel at Poltesco.

upsurge in church restorations of the period.

While the infrastructure and workforce took shape, the factory declared itself open for the purchase of stone and set about stock-piling its raw materials. At that time the quarries were mostly run by independent concerns, who leased the ground from the landlords and sold to whom they chose. At the company's invitation, they began to extract suitable blocks, load them onto the stout wooden carts drawn by carthorses, and haul them down the steep lane to the factory site. There the designers would examine them for shape, colour, and flaws, and assess their potential. They would then negotiate a price, block by block, by the roadside. Later the company made more durable arrangements with the quarries, and opened quarries of its own. A wide flat area served as a depot, and a large gantry and derrick lifted the raw stone across to the factory for initial cutting.

Even in its early stages, the factory at Poltesco caused a chilly wind to blow over the London and Penzance Serpentine Company. Their rivals had several immediate advantages.

Transport was an obvious example. Penzance had to meet the costs of carrying the stone from the Lizard quarries to the boats, unloading at Penzance harbour and transporting to Wherrytown, and the return of the finished product to the harbour for onward shipment. The weather, especially in winter, would often have caused long delays in the process. At Poltesco the materials literally came in through the back door and were wheeled out of the front, straight onto the boats.

Poltesco also competed in the market for the raw stone, driving up the price. Its lower handling costs and general convenience allowed it to match or beat Wherrytown's

Poltesco as it is today. The inscription 1866 LSCL can clearly been seen on the building.

bids at the quarries. There was probably a strong 'local' factor favouring the new enterprise. The quarry workers were mostly local Lizard men, and so were the workers at Poltesco. Who would get first pick? Whose orders would be handled first?

The Lizard's natural products were suddenly in demand, and so were its sons. Much of the general workforce in Penzance consisted of experienced serpentine workers, imported with the stone from across the bay. Some had moved over to live in the Penzance area, and others took lodgings while their families stayed behind. They were able to go home only occasionally, perhaps on foot at the weekends . Once similar work was available within easy reach of home and family, the temptation to return would have been hard to resist.

As workers defected to Poltesco, Penzance was obliged to cast around for other skilled workers to take their place in order to meet its considerable commitments. The company eventually found what it needed 'up-country', in the Blue John mines of Castleton, Derbyshire.

Blue John is a variety of fluorspar which appears to exist only in the one location in the Peak District. It has a lighter coloured base than serpentine, but an equally rich range of banded colours, from yellow through to black, many with a bluish tinge. It is found in limestone caverns and caves which are themselves a tourist attraction, and the workers used to make their products during the winter and act as guides and salesmen during the summer. The range of artefacts was very similar to the serpentine products of the Lizard – vases and urns, bowls, tazzas, candlesticks, even an occasional spectacular table top. The craft of cutting, carving and turning was also very alike in method. However the deposits were far smaller and

harder to extract, and the Blue John workings never developed into a major industry.

How the workers were tempted to Cornwall is not known, since Blue John was benefitting from the same domestic vogue as serpentine, albeit without royal endorsement. However, in 1854 six of their skilled turners were successfully head-hunted and relocated to Wherrytown with considerable publicity. By then Penzance was further relieved by the introduction of a railway service, at first indirect, which connected to the rest of the country and its markets. This allowed the company to offer a far quicker delivery than Poltesco, which always relied on shipping.

The Lizard company had also opened London offices and showrooms, at 20 Surrey Street, The Strand. With orders still pouring in, the two factories went head-to-head in competition. There was sufficient demand to keep both of them going, to employ large numbers of Cornish craftsmen, labourers, and quarriers, and to keep their backers happy and prosperous. At least for a while.

Right:
The magnificent lectern at Grade church.

Trouble

The middle Victorian years were the heyday of private enterprise, with large amounts of capital looking for suitable projects to support. It was a cut-throat era of high risk, huge profits, and spectacular failure, where competition was merciless and newcomers had to fight for their survival.

Serpentine did not arrive into an empty market niche. Its sudden appearance and novelty value encroached on long-established industries based on imported continental marble. They were not slow to take notice of the upstart stone from the Cornish wilds. Their mineralogists obtained samples for analysis and examined the quality of the competition. They were soon satisfied that it contained too many inherent flaws and weaknesses to be a serious threat, and set about publishing their results in order to besmirch its reputation.

As early as 1854, while Poltesco was still in its infancy, the *Illustrated London News* shed fascinating light on the controversy surrounding the new product, and the skirmishes already taking place regarding its quality:

Objections have been hitherto raised to serpentine as unlikely to prove durable; and seeing that the general introduction of this beautiful product may greatly interfere with the important interests of the marble trade, it is not to be wondered at that the forebodings of failure should be vehement and frequent.

The friends of serpentine meet the two principal objections of its opponents – that it is not durable in itself, and will retain neither its polish nor colour – by referring to the following facts. In the Lizard district there are three old churches of Grade, Landewednack and Ruan Minor. Many portions of these are built of blocks of granite and serpentine, alternately super-posed. They have been exposed for centuries to the blasts and storms from the Channel and the Bay of Biscay. The blocks of serpentine remain sound as when first used, with their angles sharp: whilst those of granite have, in many instances, lost both smoothness of surface and sharpness of edge.

As regards retentiveness of colour and polish, there have been produced specimens of Aberdeen granite and serpentine polished at the same time, and during eight months subjected to precisely the same influences of light, smoke, atmosphere, damp, and dryness. The colour and polish of the serpentine are alike unaffected; but both the colour and polish of the granite are gone, except on the base, which not having been exposed to the light or the atmosphere remains as it was when first subjected to the experiment.

Round One, it appeared, had gone to the Cornish. The importers and dressers of fine marble from the continent had to grind their teeth and endure the waves of praise and enthusiasm emanating from the great houses of England.

In 1860 the Lizard Serpentine Company was rubbing in its competitiveness with classical marble. Its price list offered *Chimney pieces from £5 to £150, average about the same prices as Bardilla and Rouge Royal marbles.*

There was a tempting range of more affordable products:

Polished columns

2 feet high, 3 inches diameter	£1 each
2' 6" by 3½"	£1.7s.6d
3' by 4"	£2
3'6" by 5"	£2.15s
4' by 6"	£3.15s.

Mouldings, Plinths &c, extra.

Polished slabs

per foot superficial, 1" thick	9/–
1¾" thick	12/–

Shaped work and moulded edges extra, according to design.

Had the two companies concentrated their efforts on internal fittings and ornaments only, their products would have kept their reputations intact and their markets thriving. But the serpentine, particularly the mottled red variety, was so popular that it deserved an outward show also, and it was widely used for prestigious shop fronts in the heart of London. Even the frontage of the Bank of England was once clad in it. And that was where trouble started.

The defenders of serpentine quoted in the *Illustrated London News* were perfectly correct in their claims regarding the blocks of serpentine masonry in the church towers on

The font in Cadgwith church.

the Lizard. They are still to be seen, as strong and square as when first laboriously hauled up to their resting places in the fifteenth century. But this did not take all the circumstances into account.

The church blocks are solid chunks of stone, many inches in each dimension, laid amongst other similar blocks. They were not cut into delicate wafers an inch or so thick. The environmental factors were also different. Few buildings in Britain have had to endure a greater assault from the weather than church towers on the Lizard. Winds of up to 100mph, horizontal driven rain, weeks of fog, weeks of hot clear sunshine, these had been their annual experience for four hundred years, and their lack of overt weathering is a tribute to their durability. But the maritime climate exempts the area from extremes of cold. Sometimes whole winters go by without a frost, and the hard ground frosts common to the south east of England are rare in Cornwall.

Serpentine, as seen previously is basically composed of three elements; magnesium, silicate, and approximately 14% by volume of water, trapped in its hydrated crystals. According to some observers the material is slightly plastic, expanding minutely all the time as the removal of the surrounding pressure which formed it allows the crystals to grow. The action of a hard frost on thin slices of serpentine initiated previously unknown stresses.

The most attractive stone is ribbed and shot with materials of differing chemistry and density. If the polishing of the wide surface areas of the ornamental slabs was not perfectly executed, damp was liable to penetrate. This would continue the oxidisation of trace metals, causing weaker

Mr Roberts and Mr C Bosustow at a trade exhibition at Olympia (between the wars?).

strata to dissolve between the harder areas of stone.

And finally, although the sun of the Lizard was hot and clear, the thin slabs of material were not accustomed to anything resembling the heat of a London street in high summer.

After a few years of being subjected to these forces, together with the noise and vibration of nineteenth century city traffic, some of the high profile shop fronts proudly made from the 'Cornish Marble' began, ignominiously, to crack.

Heyday

But serpentine still had far to rise before it fell. In 1862 there was another major craft exhibition in London, at which items from both factories, as well as from Pearce's workshops in Truro, were shown. They ranged from the plain – an inkstand – to the ornate, such as a figure of Apollo and a 'dolphin tazza'. Once again the orders poured in.

The Lizard had never seen anything like it.

At least eleven identifiable quarries were worked at one time or another. Some were large, employing many men with fixed machinery. A woodcut illustration of Signal Staff quarry shows an improbably large stone suspended from a wooden derrick crane on the side of the steep cliffs, with boats sailing below. At the other end of the scale were small-scale holes and scrapes in the landscape, many purely exploratory. Then as now, there is serpentine rock in plenty, some twenty square miles in area and of uncertain depth. But only a small proportion of this was suitable for working.

The most apparently promising deposits, the mass of loose boulders to be found on the beaches and in the cliffs, were ruled out by craftsmen at an early stage. The explosive events which had formed them, not to mention the battering they had regularly given each other, made them too hard and brittle to be worked without shattering.

Some of the quarries were already old, places where the original turners of ornaments had found their supplies. Serpentine had originally been quarried only for building blocks and roadstone. One quarry near Cadgwith had exported some stone to Bristol in the early nineteenth century to be ground down for the extraction of its magnesium, used in the manufacture of Epsom salts. But locations containing workable deposits of the right kind of stone were few and far between. The most notable were:

Signal Staff Quarry, Cadgwith, famous for its red striped stone.
Flagstaff Point, nearby.
Ruan Major, near the now-ruined church
Treal Quarry, by Ruan Minor
Long Alley Quarry, opened in 1854
Kellawyn and Poltesco Quarries, close to the Carleon Cove works.
Holestrow Quarry, near Kynance Cove
Balk Quarry, north of Church Cove
Gwendreath Quarry, north of Kennack Sands

Some of these contracted themselves to one or other of the manufactories on an exclusive basis. A surviving example is the lease between John Organ of Penzance and Mr CHT Hawkins for a quarry in Landewednack Parish (probably Balk Quarry) allowing him to extract up to 200 tons per year for seven years, at a rental of £10 per annum, plus 2s for every ton over the agreed 200. It was clearly a successful arrangement, for the lease was renewed after seven years at double the rent. However Mr Hawkins was as wise to the opportunity of a larger fortune as every other Cornish landlord in the nineteenth century, and the lease carefully excluded the rights to any chance discovery of tin, copper, lead or any other potentially valuable mineral of a more traditional kind.

The total number of people working in the serpentine industry at its peak is unknown, but for the first time in history labour was at

A masterpiece of work in serpentine: a clock surmounted on a carving of two dolphins, topped by a scalloped bowl on a twisted stem.

a premium on the peninsula, and people were coming into the area to work rather than drifting away, bringing all the ancillary benefits of a large regularly paid workforce to a historically poor area.

A greater draw than the hard and sometimes dangerous quarry work was the growing complex at Poltesco. From the basic core of a waterwheel attached to the remnants of a few fish-cellars, the new workshops marched towards the sea, covering more and more

ground until they reached the old circular capstan house. The fruits of its prosperity were reinvested time after time in new plant, equipment and buildings. The workforce grew from a dozen or so to as many as 65 or even more, depending on the size of the orders in hand. By the early 1860s the wheel was demoted to a secondary power source, as the company proudly installed their own steam engine. A large machine shop was built with an adjoining boiler house sporting a tall granite chimney stack.

The cove itself began to change its nature, from quiet fishing beach to an industrial landscape, full of noise, smoke, discarded equipment, spoil tips, depots of stone, coal, timber and straw for packaging, dust everywhere, ringing to the sound of saws, chisels, hammers and nails, the chugging of the steam engine, the rumbling of the wheel, the grinding and sanding of the stone, the shouting of orders and the human sounds of men at work, against the constant background of the sea beating on the shingle.

Next to the workshops was the complex of offices, and next to the capstan house was built a fine three-storey warehouse, doubling as a showroom, where the finished articles were either displayed or stored ready for shipping. At the top of its gabled face a stone was proudly carved with the inscription 'LSCL 1866' to mark the mighty achievements of the Lizard Serpentine Company Ltd.

The output included every possible marble product, from plain tablets and columns to delicately inlaid clocks and table tops, even candelabra. Visitors to the London showrooms were greeted by an impressive 7'6" classical urn displayed in the foyer. Exports went as far as Paris and Rome. Local families also sought the prestige of a serpentine objet d'art. Lanhydrock House, for example, the home of the Robartes family, ordered a number of items including an obelisk, a table, urns and tazzas.

Churches were also in the market. Many of them were undergoing large scale revival and refurbishment – Grade Church near

The pulpit at Grade church.

Cadgwith, for example, was virtually rebuilt in 1862 – and the vogue for the native stone led to orders for ornate lecterns, pulpits, fonts, columns to support existing fonts, headstones and smaller details.

Poltesco prospered, and as well as its own industrial buildings a fine house was built, mainly of dressed serpentine, for the manager Henry Cox. It was pleasantly tucked into the sheltered side of the valley just above the artificial lagoon.

The LSCL gained the commercial edge over its Penzance rivals and soon overtook them altogether. Its steep expansion was matched by a proportionate contraction of Wherrytown's trade, despite its railway links and royal connections. There is no sentiment in business, and after a few difficult years the London & Penzance Serpentine Company was wound up in 1865, and the Wherrytown factory closed its doors.

However Penzance's association with serpentine was far from over. The factory and its engine had to be abandoned, the London backers disappeared and the Penzance workforce fragmented, but they regrouped into several substantial independent concerns, including the Drew and Stevens families. They could no longer compete for the large scale monumental work, but they were skilled, experienced and resourceful. Their output varied from fine art carving, to humbler items more befitting the new market which had arrived in the wake of the railway.

Going to the seaside had become a popular Victorian fad. The West Country was originally seen as a mild wintering place for the wealthy, who spent their summers in France and Italy. But the railways brought the opportunity for affordable travel, and the waters of Mount's Bay were suddenly within a day's journey for the burgeoning middle classes. As serpentine was being shipped in one direction, tourists were arriving in the other. Penzance built a promenade for them to walk along – beaches still being considered unsuitable for their clothes – and the Queen's Hotel was built to accommodate them, followed by others. Penzance is effectively two towns, the market centre and the seafront, and it was on the seafront that the serpentine workers plied their trade.

The visitors' requirements did not stretch to heavy or expensive items. They wanted souvenirs, inexpensive, portable, and somehow typical of the far-flung region they had visited. From fulfilling bespoke commissions, the ex-Wherrytown workers now addressed their craft to satisfying the new demand. They built up stocks of saleable items suitable for the casual buyer. In 1883 it was recorded that five serpentine workshops were busy in the Penzance area. Their devotion to the souvenir trade had not extinguished their skill in fine art, as demonstrated by Charles Stevens of Penzance who sent a carving of *an anchor circled by a dolphin surmounted by a bowl* to the Victoria and Albert Museum as late as 1900.

As for the factory, it became the headquarters for the local artillery and enjoyed a brief vogue as a roller skating rink, before being demolished in 1916 to make way for the Bedford-Bolitho gardens. The skating element has endured to this day, and a skateboard park stands where the serpentine was once worked.

On the Lizard Poltesco ploughed on. Its only recorded set back had been the loss of a ship laden with finished product in 1861, but it weathered that loss and became a fixture in the area, forging ahead through twenty years of expansion, providing secure employment to a whole generation of Lizard workers.

Decline and Fall

For any commercial adventure in minerals the earliest years will be the most profitable. The serpentine trade did not have to meet the enormous challenges of the tin and copper mines, where deeper and deeper delving required increasingly ingenious mechanical solutions to the problems of extraction, transport and drainage. But the highly coloured serpentine rocks were essentially small seams in a larger mineral complex, and the endless demand for large unflawed pieces eventually exhausted the supplies of one quarry after another. Increasing scarcity meant that costs rose, and so did prices.

The news of its poor weathering qualities had spread through the small gossipy world of architects and designers, and the importers of continental marbles pressed home their advantage. The Great Exhibition was now a memory, and the attention of the Royal Family had long since moved on. Serpentine was no longer a novelty but an increasingly expensive and somewhat tarnished commodity.

In 1870 the first major crisis occurred at Poltesco. The venerable Henry Cox left, and set up his own business in Cadgwith. The original Lizard Serpentine Company was wound up, and the factory business was re-launched under the title of the Poltesco Marble Company Ltd – notably omitting the

A model made all in serpentine of the proposed sunday school –
made by the lighthouse keeper to raise money for the project.

word 'serpentine'. It wisely concentrated on manufacturing items for interior use only, under the management of William Bazie Simons. The workforce was reduced and the new company trimmed its sails to the core business for which a good demand still existed – fireplaces, mantlepieces, pillars, and classical ornaments.

Gradually the labour force was slimmed down to a rump of about twenty workers, and the range of products began to look – as in Penzance – more down market. Among the many travellers and 'explorers' of Cornwall who were publishing their adventures in the late nineteenth century, Mrs Dinah Craik recounted her visit to Poltesco in 1881:

At Poltesco are the principal serpentine works, the one commerce of the district. The monotonous hum of its machinery mingled oddly with the murmur of the trout stream which ran through the pretty little valley, crossed by a wooden bridge where a solitary angler stood fishing in imperturbable content.

There were only about a dozen workmen visible, one of whom came forward and explained to us the mode of work; afterwards taking us to the showroom, which contained everything possible to be made from serpentine, from mantlepieces and tombstones down to brooches and studs. Very delicate and beautiful was the workmanship.

Mrs Craik's transaction with the factory, however, set the tone for the future:

We departed, taking only a few little ornaments. We should have liked to carry off a cart-load – especially two enormous vases and a chimney-piece – but travellers have limits to luggage, and to purse as well.

Another upheaval in the company's organisation and fortunes led to its takeover

by a merchant and monumental mason from Mile End, London, Mr Jabez Druitt. Perhaps preferring the arcadian bliss of the *pretty little valley* to the smog and bustle of Victorian London's East End, he took a lease on the factory in the same year as Mrs Craik's visit. The factory may have been reduced, hardly a shadow of its former might, but his enterprise was not wasted. The market for serpentine products was still worthwhile and the attenuated business continued for another twelve years.

However the twin pressures of diminishing demand and increasingly expensive and unreliable supply could only end one way. In 1893, following the loss of another uninsured sea cargo of finished articles, the *monotonous hum* of the machinery fell silent for the last time. One of Cornwall's major – now almost forgotten – manufacturing enterprises succumbed to the fate of so many others, and reached the end of its commercial viability. For thirty years of meteoric rise and gradual decline, it had contributed incalculably to the fame and prosperity of the region, and left a legacy of finely crafted articles which graced

Vase, clock, euchre trump marker, lighthouse with compass and ikon to St John the Baptist.

many houses, churches and museums. In Carleon Cove the stream, the gulls, the wind, and the waves were once more the only sounds to disturb the peace.

The abandoned factory underwent a long and sad demise. Writer after amateur writer, breezily penning their experiences of England's most southerly peninsula in tones of wonder, was struck to silence by the sight. After walking the coast path from Lizard Point, and tasting the rustic charm of Cadgwith, they turned a corner to find themselves suddenly facing a vision of post-industrial despair, as grim and sordid as any to be found in their home cities. Without maintenance the workshop roofs soon succumbed to weathering and vandalism. Machinery of any value had been sold off, but everything else had been abandoned where it was when production ceased. The occasional use of the wheel for cutting straw and the use of the few sound sheds as *the habitation of swine* only emphasised the air of desolation. The scene was well described by the writer Arthur Symons, who rented a cottage at Poltesco in 1904 and 1905. Of Carleon Cove he wrote:

I never linger there. It is disfeatured and defeated, an ugly gash in the cliff-side. There is always something gloomy and uncomfortable in its cramped bed of pebbles, the great dark cliff, covered thinly with green turf, which rises to so steep a height above it, and the broken and deserted sheds, chimneys and waterwheel where the serpentine factory had been. The water still runs along a wooden tray from the river to the great wheel, and sometimes by accident the rusty thing begins to turn with a ghastly clanking, like a dead thing galvanised into some useless and unnatural semblance of life. The place is uncanny, like all solitary places which men have spoiled and then deserted.

During the Great War some of the factory was requisitioned as a carpenters' workshop and more incongruously as a children's playroom. By 1917 the wooden spokes of the 25' wheel were dangerously rotten and it was taken down. Its mighty iron hoops were loaded up on carts and taken away for scrap. Between the wars the factory site was considered as a possibility for a holiday complex, and a developer went as far as to clear the site with explosives, sparing only the great warehouse. But nothing further came of it, and the valley

was left to its ghosts. Only a few reminders – most poignantly a great stone set in the ground, and marked with innumerable grooves where slabs had been set for saw-cutting – bore witness to its extraordinary and illustrious past.

Carleon House had been leased to the factory manager, Mr Herbert Cohen, in 1889, and his daughter bought it from the estate, living there until 1947. The house and the whole area now belong to the National Trust.

A stone set in the ground at Poltesco, marked with grooves where slabs had been set for saw-cutting.

To the Lighthouse

It seemed that the story of serpentine was over. Like many a fashion it had grown too fast, flowered, wilted and died.

Its legacy was to be found all around the country and in other parts of the world. To modern eyes the dark slabs of cold, glossy marble may represent Victorian taste at its worst – its fascination with the classical, its love of the massive and adamant, its rigid pomposity. Even the ornamental church-work is not immune to such temptations, especially the desire to use as many different varieties of stone as possible in the same piece. But many of the products of Poltesco and Penzance were admirable by any standards, delicately coloured, beautifully finished, sometimes exquisitely carved, rivalling the marble craft of any other European manufacturer.

That era was unquestionably over. The promiscuous use of the stone over thirty years for monumental urns, vases, slabs and columns had left the quarries virtually exhausted, certainly as far as large unflawed deposits were concerned. Even if the stone had been available, setting up another factory would have been commercial madness. Public tastes were changing. By all logic, the working of serpentine should have slipped back into the footnotes of history.

But long before it became an industry, it had been a historic local craft. Even when industrial demand had sucked in most of the established workers to produce items themselves and to instruct others, a few remained behind. Declining the temptation of high wages and as much work as they could handle, they had carried on as they always

Above: Miss Agnes Roberts and Samuel Jose standing outside the shop which is now Shipton's Stone Shop.

Below: Wilfred William Shipton at his lathe in the late 1940s.

had. Mostly based in the Lizard village, the turning of serpentine remained a vernacular trade, passed on from father to son.

As the factories declined, the stone workers who did not join the great diaspora leaving Cornwall to seek their fortunes abroad seeped back into the traditional business, setting up individual workshops and small co-operatives here and there on the peninsula. The fine London showrooms were now an unreal memory, and there was no longer an established network or market for their products. Instead they went back to basics.

In a nutshell the basics of their trade were (and still are): that the coloured serpentine was unique, not only to Cornwall but to their particular area; that they possessed the skill to work it into whatever shapes and objects would attract their customers; that their customers would often like something which reminded them of the area they had visited;

and that their market would consist almost entirely of holiday visitors. Except for the occasional local commission, there was no longer any point in producing anything especially ornate, large or expensive. From being creators of pulpits for the church, table-tops for royalty, and the fascia of the Bank of England, they would in future be restricted to the manufacture of holiday souvenirs.

The Cornish are pragmatic, well used to fluctuations of fortune. For centuries they had experienced the roller coaster of tin and copper mining, from famine to feast and back again. Now the massive deposits discovered in the Far East had undercut domestic mineral prices to a ruinous degree. The mines were failing all around them, never to revive. The diaspora had become a flood, and the population of Cornwall was declining fast. Whole villages became quiet and destitute. Poverty, the workhouse or exile faced family after family.

A very beautifully crafted bowl.

Against such a background, those with a trade still worth following shed few tears over their loss of prestige. The rump of the serpentine workers made the most of their only advantage with all the skill they possessed. When necessary they picked up what other bits of work presented themselves, whether in fishing, farming, labouring in the many public works being undertaken, delivering the mail, taking in visitors, keeping a pony and trap for hire on the long and twisty Lizard roads, or any other supplementary income which could be scraped together. But their core business was to spend much of the winter stock-piling serpentine souvenirs, and most of the summer selling them for much-needed cash.

The Lizard was rarely the primary destination of holiday travellers, who were more likely to be seduced by the beauty of Mount's Bay or the artists' colony at St Ives. But the area was no longer unknown. Rev CA Johns'

delightful book *Two Weeks at the Lizard*, published in 1848, had paved the way for many other early enthusiasts. The appeal rested not only on the magnificence of its coastal scenery but also on the unique geology, which was a Victorian fascination, and its exceptional flora, which was another. Travellers reported in glowing terms the peace and tranquillity, the small wildflowers and heathers clinging to life on the plateau, the picturesque charm of Cadgwith, Coverack and St Keverne, the elemental grandeur of Kynance. Tennyson was only one of many to be seduced by its wonders.

Welcome as they were, these studious and articulate pioneers were hardly the stuff of a mass market. Just when this was needed most, providence intervened in the form of the Helston Railway Company.

This worthy local enterprise formed an association with the Great Western Railway

A pair of vases with their bill.

to build a small branch line from the Paddington to Penzance trunk route at a desolate rural depot between Camborne and Hayle, Gwinear Road. The hope was that the line would bear a good deal of freight to and from the largely agricultural Helston area, and that it would prove popular with local passengers and holidaymakers. And so it turned out. The Helston branch line was opened on 9th May 1887, giving a second day of celebrations to follow Helston's most famous annual tradition, Flora (or Furry) Day.

From the outset the backers envisaged that the line would eventually continue on to the Lizard point, and designed Helston's station as a through station rather than a terminus. To complete the task they required a further £100,000 and two more years' hard work. The line would have been one of the most spectacular in Britain, and its effect on the Lizard village can only be imagined. The Great Western Railway was a vast and diverse concern, which, as well as running a railway, owned land, built hotels, ran bus services and concerned itself with every aspect of the holiday trade which it did so much to promote. Wherever the railway touched a picturesque

coastal destination, a holiday resort grew. The tiny fishing port of Newquay, for example, was virtually recreated by the GWR.

Helston Station brought the mainstream of holiday traffic within an easy ride of the peninsula, and when in 1903 the GWR set up its own regular and successful bus service there seemed no justification for the extra expense of extending the line. A steady stream of day trippers and longer-term visitors found the pleasures of the Lizard easily accessible, and responded with enthusiasm.

On the most spectacular headlands, before conservation or rural planning was even a concept, hotels and large private houses emerged like medieval castles. More modest hotels and guest houses opened for business. A tourist boom, tiny by modern standards but highly significant to a newly impoverished region, was born.

The fame of the Lizard spread further The area's most celebrated – if fictional – visitors were much affected by the landscape, but provided little by way of good copy for a holiday brochure:

A gull on a rock, calendars of Polperro and Land's End, a lighthouse cigarette lighter, a mushroom and piskey and a nutcracker.

It was a singular spot, and one particularly suited to the grim humour of my patient. ...We looked down on the whole sinister semicircle of Mount's Bay, that old death-trap of sailing vessels ... the wise mariner stands far out from that evil place...

On the land side our surroundings were as sombre as on the sea. It was a country of rolling moors, lonely and dun-coloured, with an occasional church tower to mark the site of some old-world village. ...The glamour and mystery of the place, with its sinister atmosphere of forgotten nations, appealed to the imagination of my friend, and he spent much of his time in long walks and solitary meditations...

(Arthur Conan Doyle – *The Adventure of the Devil's Foot* from *His Last Bow*).

Most visitors were unaware of serpentine's former industrial history, indeed unaware of its very existence until they encountered it in the local shops. Like any travellers they were attracted by something uniquely ethnic. The craftsmen and their wives and families had years of experience in the art of selling serpentine wares, and knew their business well. The new influx encouraged innovations in design. No potential artefact was too mundane if a demand could be identified, and many new lines were added to the traditional candlesticks and vases. Ashtrays were a promising and easily produced example, together with cruet sets, calendar holders, little pill or jewel boxes with lids, tobacco jars, bowls, and smaller trinkets. Some incorporated other mass produced products,

An ornate fireplace in the more unusual green serpentine.

such as clocks and barometers.

However none of these objects, however beautifully produced, spoke uniquely of Cornwall. Some objects were embellished with stuck-on legends, photographs or even engravings to make up this deficiency. But the best solution came in the inspired design of serpentine's most famous and iconic form.

No-one knows who first came up with the idea, or even which lighthouse was the template for the original design. Two lighthouses have been identified as the model – the Eddystone at Plymouth and the lonely Bishop Rock to the west of the Isles of Scilly, but sea-based lighthouses are necessarily much alike. For the craftsmen it was a welcome design. It was relatively easy to execute, with no thin or ornate edges to chip and crack, a highly suitable format for the softer specimens of stone. The models ranged in size from tiny to a few huge examples, made for display rather than sale. Their complexity varied also, from simple columns to more detailed objects, often sitting on a base of unpolished natural stone, sometimes even cut with minuscule steps and other details.

The lighthouse was exactly what the visitors sought. Britons always respond to the romance of the sea, and lighthouses have a special place in this pantheon. The humanity of their purpose, the strange and artificially isolated life-style of their operators, the defiant statement of their very existence in the face of the fury of the sea, all lodged them in the public consciousness. They were almost quasi-religious in their symbolism, the 'light shining in the darkness', warning unknown strangers of unseen hazards. The legendary feat of Grace Darling, and dramatic contemporary novels like *The Watchers on the Longships* reinforced their sentimental status. The opportunity to purchase a reminder of these deep-seated emotions in a stone unique

to the Cornish peninsula was irresistible. The lighthouse design became a bestseller; and still is. For many people it is the first (and often only) image which the word 'serpentine' conjures.

Later the lighthouses were fitted with glass windows, and later still the core of the model was bored through to allow a wire, and the lighthouses were fitted with their own electric lights, destined to shine out over many a suburban sideboard.

Hundreds of thousands were produced, finding homes on shelves and mantlepieces all over Britain, and elsewhere, a little piece of the Lizard telling a story of human endeavour. They were a runaway success, and led the way for the survival of the turner's craft.

An unusually marked bowl with lid.

Survival

Relying entirely on a regular supply of visitors with cash to spend, the turners went through many variations of fortune as the twentieth century progressed. The popularity of the railways and the bus service – motor charabancs replacing the horse-drawn carriages – led to a stream of visitors. The Lizard appealed to writers in particular, many of them eminent. As well as Conan Doyle, Rupert Brooke, Oscar Wilde, Bernard Shaw, and Virginia Woolf all recorded time spent there.

Lizard Town itself was growing, with a school, chapel, lifeboat station, post office, even a reading room. Its strategic position led to a

regular influx of outsiders. Coastguards, lighthouse keepers and later the Lloyds' Signal Station staff were stationed there. One of the most notable settlers was of course Guglielmo Marconi, who made it his base. His achievements began with a successful wireless message from the Lizard to the Isle of Wight in early 1901, and ended with the first ever transatlantic communication from Poldhu to Newfoundland later the same year.

The First World War took its toll from Landewednack parish as it did from every other. Local men marched away, but many others marched into the village to take their place. Before ship's radio and radar, England's

Serpentine beer pumps and ashtrays at the Top House pub, Lizard Town.

The stages of turning a bowl by John Hendy.

1: a rough stem is knocked out to shape with a chipping hammer and stuck onto the face plate or chuck of the lathe.

2: the basic shape is further roughed out on the lathe using chisels with tungsten carbon tips.

most southerly point carried a huge responsibility for monitoring channel shipping. The coastguard stations were on permanent watch, recording naval movements, sending and receiving signals, looking out for the momentary flash of a submarine's periscope, watching at night for spies. As air power became more significant and the first airfields were established on the peninsula, the skies too had to be searched. Unlike so many villages which emptied of men altogether, the Lizard remained busy.

After the war a new breed of tourist began to make its first overtures, the first thin trickle which would become the unstoppable flood of private motorists. More and more guide books appeared, describing the itinerary of West Cornwall by bus or 'tourer', in which the Lizard peninsula was always noted as being worth a visit. Once again commentators excepted the unfortunate Lizard Town from their generally complimentary reports, and SPB Mais, writing for the GWR in 1928, was equally unenchanted by its most famous export:

The Lizard village ...is a stopping-place only....a

dreary collection of workshops in which are made those streaked souvenirs of lighthouses and Cornish crosses, with which the unthinking tourist desires to cumber himself.

The turners were immune to such haughty judgements. As long as the cavalcade of *unthinking tourists* persisted they would find suitable wares with which to *cumber* them. Even throughout the lean years of the 1930s, enough of them found their way there to keep the craft alive.

As another war loomed, the village again assumed a strategic importance. Service personnel poured into the area, including two divisions of Americans. A radar station was established at Bass Point, and a large new airfield was constructed at Predannack. Once more the native craftsmen – those who had not been called up themselves – kept the trade going between their other wartime duties.

After the war, Predannack was abandoned as an airfield. Part of it became a research station where Sir Barnes Wallis worked on swing-wing supersonic aircraft, and one Nissen hut was taken over by his friend

3: the inside is hollowed out and the outside is further cut out.

4: the bowl is polished inside and turned further outside to its final shape.

Leonard Cheshire as his first Cheshire Home. The loss of military personnel was more than restored by the establishment of the huge RNAS airfield at Culdrose. As so many times in its history, just when the serpentine trade seemed doomed to decline, something turned up to save it.

By the late 1950s, post-war prosperity ensured that the 'something' became the biggest boom since the glory years of Poltesco. Mass tourism by rail and car really took off. Foreign travel was still in the future, reserved for the adventurous few, and coastal resorts all over England experienced a demand which exceeded their wildest dreams. Holiday camps sprang up on the Lizard, often utilising the abandoned service quarters all over the peninsula, and a caravan park opened at Kennack Sands. Every spare bedroom became a B&B, every resort churned out

5: the bowl has its final polishing both inside and out before being cut off from the chuck.

industrial quantities of ice cream and fish and chips, and every other shed became a souvenir shop. The Helston branch line closed in 1962, but this did little to diminish the tide of visitors. Their capacity for souvenirs was unprecedented. They were unsophisticated travellers, and were content with almost anything they could take home to family and friends, as long as it was clearly marked with its Cornish origin.

They swarmed over the serpentine shops. The turners were under pressure to produce the goods, and recruited extra help. Up to forty of them worked full time to meet demand at the Lizard alone. With so many undiscriminating buyers, quantity took over from quality, and the trade followed its customers down-market. In Penzance, where families of turners had also contrived to keep their trade alive through the hard times, serpentine was also an 'overnight' success. Some seafront cottages, in particular near the old works at Wherrytown, sold souvenirs from their front porches, and one or two shops opened primarily to sell them. Other stone shops appeared in every resort in Cornwall, selling not only serpentine but many other decorative and polished minerals. Seashells stuck together in appealing shapes found a ready market. Almost anything would do.

It had to be available when required, as the harvest time was brief. The bulk of the visitors came from the factories of the north, and their holidays tended to be squeezed into the same few weeks. The whole summer season lasted barely three months. By the first week in September, as if someone had blown a whistle, the streets emptied and nearly everyone had gone. The souvenir trade then had somehow to keep the wolf from the door for the remaining forty weeks, until the

manic rush began all over again.

It could not last. Cornwall's unpredictable summer weather saw to that. After a few years of roaming the grey Cornish streets in plastic macs leading bedraggled and fractious children, the British public took to cheaper continental holidays with a sigh of relief. The Cornish holiday trade took a steep dive, and the demand for souvenirs declined accordingly. Second generation tourists arrived, more sophisticated and streetwise, no longer satisfied with any old thing that was thrust at them, either in quality of accommodation, food, facilities, or local crafts. They were especially resistant to the sort of tat their parents had fallen for. Holiday souvenirs were seen – per se – as naff.

Serpentine – for the second time in its trading history – was losing its reputation.

A beautiful chess set and board with a drawer made by John Hendy as a labour of love for his father.

Digging for Serpentine

These photographs taken by Peter Greenslade show the most recent digging for serpentine, in the late 1990s, done by a collective group of the then seven active workers from the Lizard. Agreement had to be reached with the owners of the land and English Nature who are the custodians of much of the Lizard peninsula. With new technology – a JCB –it is possible to rework old sites where previously men had only been able to dig with picks and spades.

1: First the heather and bracken are carefully taken off and put to one side; to be replaced when the site is made good.

Above 2: The bottom of old workings is found – checking over the spoils before digging deeper. It fills with water quickly.

Below 3: Working much deeper with a 'ripper' on the JCB. This allows the driver to work carefully between the serpentine 'layers' causing as little damage to the rocks as possible. It is mainly clay between the stone.

Above 4: Drawing good clean stone – this turned out to be a good productive site – the stone is sorted and split.

Below 5: Rock is sorted into equal piles – which are drawn by lots – here one lot is being loaded – everyone working as a team.

6: The site after the material is carefully infilled layer by layer with the vegetation put back – within a year it was restored to fig 1.

Present and Future

In the 1860s there were well over one hundred; in the 1950s thirty or forty; in 1970 sixteen; in 1985, nine; and in 2005 just a handful of people making a full time living from Lizard serpentine. Only John Hendy, Michael and Ian Casley, David Hill and his nephew, James who is learing the trade and Derek Pitman currently keep alive this ancient tradition. Some of the younger generation are showing enthusiasm for carrying on the trade, but many obstacles stand in their way. The principal problem is, once more, the shortage of workable stone. The twentieth century boom accounted for many tons of what was already in short supply.

As well as good colour, the crucial factor is the hardness of the raw material. Turning serpentine, the professional turners modestly claim, is not complicated. The natural blocks are rough-hewn to shapes suitable for the lathe, and are then worked down by simple tools, similar to wood turning chisels, to the desired shape. The shiny surface on the finished item is not artificial but the natural property of the stone, laboriously sanded down with 'wet and dry' sandpaper, polished up using olive oil and jeweller's rouge, and buffed, preferably with corduroy, to a high gloss. Through this surface the web of original colours, swirls, crystals, impurities, minerals, veins and pathways reflect the frozen history within the rock.

A sculpture of a fish – the fish being polished and carved out of a piece of stone.

The lathes are now worked with electricity instead of foot-treadles, and the dust is caught with extractors instead of settling like a snow-storm on the operator, but otherwise the technique has not changed. A major part of the turner's skill resides in assessing the unprepossessing chunks of rock in his yard and knowing what to make from them, whether a lighthouse, an egg, a vase or a clock, understanding how the veins will run, the range of hardness and softness, the likely colour, the chance of interior faults. It takes a lifetime's knowledge and experience.

But most serpentine deposits, even on the Lizard, are monotonous in colour, darkening down almost to black, and too hard to work by hand. The good stone is running out. Prospecting continues, but it now properly takes place under strict environmental supervision. All sites of investigation and abstraction have to be back-filled and restored to their natural state. So far no new site of any promise has emerged, and the deposits remaining in the old quarries are scant and inaccessible.

The trade does not appear attractive to the young. Like any rural craft, the years required to learn it properly and the tedium of sticking at it for a lifetime prove too demanding for a quicker generation. In these less rigorous times the young have many options, matters

David Hill.

John Hendy.

of choice rather than survival.

The decline of the trade is all the more poignant since the quality of the finished serpentine products has risen once again. They are still essentially mass produced souvenirs, and basic lines are still on offer, but the cheap tourist fodder of the middle twentieth century is now a memory. The overall impression when visiting any of the existing serpentine shops is of a more thoughtful and artistic approach to the material. It is impossible now to travel through Cornwall without being solicited by art and craft galleries at every turn, and serpentine products have to stand up in a more informed aesthetic environment. Their current ranges show how well they are meeting this challenge.

This approach may be a pointer to future survival. Most of the traditional turners, as a change from of turning out identical items, have made individual pieces for their own pleasure, to stretch their craft or to provide an eye-catching display. Mostly these are carved rather than turned – a huge lighthouse, an elaborate font, a complete chess set and board, often hidden, private creations. Many of the new tourists are buyers of fine art and craft, with the purchasing power to reward a more artistic approach. There is a growing market for more individual pieces which demonstrate the beauty of the stone and the unique skill of those who work in it. Serpentine is already attracting the attention of a new generation of fine-art sculptors. At the other extreme (of size) some

Derek Pitman.

Ian Casley.

Michael Casley.

delightful jewellery is being made from the smallest pieces of stone. It may be that once again a last minute reprieve is on the horizon

Serpentine is not limited to the Lizard peninsula, or to one use only. In America they make brooches and gemstones out of the several varieties of rock available in the many shades of serpentine green. The stone is used in industry, for example in brake linings and in the culture of antibiotics. A new and potentially significant process is currently being investigated using ground serpentine as an effective means to 'lock up' carbon dioxide emissions. On the other extreme it has reputed mystical qualities, being especially associated with a fulfilled old age.

Even if all human actyivity in this material came to an end, visitors to Kynance Cove could still turn their backs on the sea, and gaze at the story laid out before them. Now peaceful, it records millions of years of elemental violence and savage beauty, from the blood-tipped crags of the cliff face to the multi-hued rocks on the beach to the round black boulders in the secret cave pools where sea otters used to play. It is a true wonder of the world.

Miniature pieces made by Derek Pitman –
see the 50p piece in the middle.

The Serpentine Trail

Anyone wishing to follow the story of serpentine for themselves should first obtain *Beneath The Skin of The Lizard* by Robin Bates & Bill Scolding, published by Cornwall County Council. It is an exemplary piece of work, setting out the geological history of the peninsula and translating it into a highly accessible journey of exploration, with photographs, diagrams, and clear uncluttered language, presented as seven different walks around the area. It was my own guide in beginning to understand the area, and I would recommend it to all.

The other 'Walks' in the same series are all worth reading, as is the Lizard History Society's publication *The Lizard In Landewednack*.

Armed with these books and a good OS map there is no better way to discover the serpentine trail than by walking it yourself. The scenery is truly awe-inspiring, and – even for those with a minimal interest in geology – the insight into the making of the earth's surface is fascinating.

Once your eye is in for serpentine, you will see it everywhere. The church towers of Mullion, Ruan Minor, Grade, and Landewednack (the Lizard Town's parish church) are largely composed of great blocks of it, the dark variety, hard enough to weather for five hundred years with hardly a blemish. Many of the old farmhouses and cottages are also made from it, as are some of the chapels, and modern houses now seem to pride themselves on its use as cladding stone. Mullion is the best village of all for serpentine spotting. Out in the countryside it is in the hedges, and forms most of the old gateposts and stiles within its natural area.

Many of the churches display serpentine artefacts. Lonely Grade church, set in the open fields of the plateau has a multicoloured serpentine lectern and some beautiful pillars set into its integral pulpit. Landewednack has a similar lectern, and a pulpit fronted by sheets of red serpentine. Its doorway within the porch is graced by two grooved red serpentine pillars, a rare example

Poltesco.

The lectern at St Wynwallow church, Landewednack.

of the ornamental use of the stone in its unpolished state. Other churches have smaller details, mainly polished columns, often in the supports of the font. One is in the humble, beautiful church of St Mary in Cadgwith, a church made not of granite and serpentine but of timber and corrugated iron. Several of the churchyards feature serpentine headstones.

Lizard Town still has few pretensions, but is worth a whole day on its own. The ground beneath it is not serpentine, but it seems that almost everything else there is. There are turners' workshops to be seen open and working, and several showrooms full of their labours. Church Cove and Landewednack church are a short walk to the east and Kynance Cove a slightly stiffer one to the west. There are good places to eat and drink, and beautiful views on every side. And you can park.

Finally anyone interested in this story should not miss a visit to Poltesco. Walk there if you

A serpentine stile at Grade church.

Turners' workshops are small, like this one on Lizard point. There used to be many more – you can see them boarded up.

can – the road down is narrow and single track, with very limited parking. Far better to stop in Ruan Minor or Kuggar and stroll down, or approach via the coast path. The Poltesco valley is as lovely a walk as any in Cornwall, unspoiled, full of trees, with a working water mill halfway down. In Carleon Cove the huge factory warehouse remains, butted into the old capstan-house, but the rest of that mighty enterprise lies as it fell, with sections of the old chimney stack in the undergrowth where it was dynamited in the 1930s. The outlines of the factory are easy to see, the pit where the huge wheel once revolved, the cutting-stone with its tracery of grooves. It has shaken off its ghostly qualities now, and remains a peaceful if solemn reminder of a great human enterprise, come and gone.

Bibliography

Bates, Robin & Scolding, Bill *Beneath the Skin of The Lizard* 2000 Cornwall County Council
Bates, Robin & Scolding, Bill *Five Walks from The Lizard* Cornwall County Council
Bates, Robin & Scolding, Bill *Five Walks Around Ruan Minor & Cadgwith* Cornwall County Council
Conan Doyle, Arthur *His Last Bow*
Craik, Mrs, *An Unsentimental Journey Through Cornwall,* 1884
Johns, Rev CA *Two Weeks at The Lizard* 1848
Johns, Charles *Poltesco Valley, Cornwall Preliminary Archaeological & Historical Survey,* 2003 Cornwall Archaeological Unit
Mais, SPB, *Cornish Riviera,* 1928
Ollerenshaw, Arthur E *The History of Blue John Stone* Eva M & GS Ollerenshaw & RJ & D Harrison, Castleton, England

Church Trails In Cornwall The Diocese of Cornwall
The Lizard in Landewednack 1996 The Lizard History Society
The Geology of The Lizard & Meneage 1946 HMSO Geological Survey of Great Britain

Other sources from guidebooks, articles, parish records, and the internet.

The font in St Mary's chuch, Penzance, carved by Joseph
Brown from serpentine rock in memory of
John Matthews 1807–71, Borough Surveyor 1849–69.